What to do when you can't add and subtract

by Steve Chinn

EGON PUBLISHERS LTD

Title: What to do when you can't add and subtract
Author: Steve Chinn

ISBN 1899998 31 4

First Published in Great Britain 1999
by Egon Publishers Ltd.
Royston Road, Baldock
Herts. SG7 6NW

Design by Climacs Imagin, Royston Road, Baldock, Herts. SG7 6NW

Printed in England by Halstan & Co. Ltd., Amersham, Bucks.

ABOUT THIS BOOK

In 'everyday' life you are most likely to use addition and subtraction more than any other mathematics procedure. This book carefully explains addition and subtraction so that you have every chance of understanding and remembering how to do these two bits of mathematics.

The book uses effective learning methods, often using multi-sensory techniques (using input to the brain via speaking, listening, writing and seeing). Each input helps to make learning more efficient.

The book also tries to create visual images to help learning.

The 'What to do when you can't...' mathematics books are written for parents and teachers who want to know how to help children understand and learn and for older learners who need clear explanations to rebuild skills.

Although there are practise examples throughout the book, it is not a book of exercises. There is a good selection of 'work / exercise' books in shops. These will help consolidate learning, but this book is the start. It is designed to teach.

Look at the ideas. Think about them. Practise them. Gain confidence. Learn successfully.

Steve Chinn

There are some ideas for study strategies within the book, but one of the best pieces of advice is

"Do a little (but not too little) work often"

When reading through sections use the study technique of:

- Skim/overview....get the general picture.
- Then read in detail.
- Do the practical work.
- Read again to confirm your understanding.
- Try the practise examples.
- Skim/overview to top up your memory.

Contents

+ADDING AND SUBTRACTING-

Basically adding is putting together.

Basically subtracting is taking apart.

This makes them opposite versions of the same procedure.

Examples.

$$6 + 3 = 9$$
$$9 - 3 = 6$$

Adding 6 and 3 gives 9. Taking 3 from 9 takes you back to 6.

$$20 + 4 = 24$$
$$24 - 4 = 20$$

Adding 20 and 4 gives 24. Taking 4 from 24 takes you back to 20.

$$43 + 18 = 61$$
$$61 - 18 = 43$$

Adding 43 and 18 gives 61. Taking 18 from 61 takes you back to 43.

Try the 9, 6, 3 example with coins or counters.

Put out 6 counters and 3 counters.

Put them together (add) to give 9.

Take away (subtract) 3 counters to leave 6.

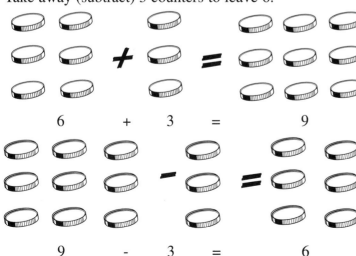

6   +   3   =   9

9   -   3   =   6

This book is designed to be used . For example, use highlighter pens to pick out the bits you feel are most important to you. There are notes from me (S.C.) in some margins, but the main function of the margins is to give you space to make notes.

Numbers within numbers

When coins are used in this book to illustrate numbers, they are shown in patterns, based on an arrangement of 5

This grouping helps when adding because it enables you to see the amounts more quickly and it also shows when 10 is formed.

For example: 7+8=15

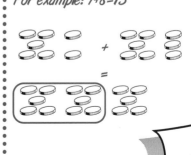

BASIC ADDITION AND SUBTRACTION FACTS
(Also called number bonds.)

It will be a great help with addition and subtraction sums if you can memorise or learn to quickly work out these basic addition and subtraction facts (even if you can finger count them, the strategies described below will be better).

If you have to learn a maths fact it is a good idea to make it worth as much as possible. This idea applies well to addition facts, for example;

Each addition fact is actually two addition facts and two subtraction facts.

For example;

$$6 + 4 = 10$$

is also $\quad 4 + 6 = 10$

and $\quad 10 - 4 = 6$

and $\quad 10 - 6 = 4$

There are 121 basic addition facts. Approximately half are commutative (which means complementary) such as $4 + 5 = 9$ and $5 + 4 = 9$. This reduces the learning task to around 60 facts.

Most of the facts can be inter-related or greatly simplified.

Try the 6+4=4+6 idea with coins!

These 121 addition facts are mirrored by 121 subtraction facts, so, for example 4 + 5 = 9 and 5 + 4 = 9 are mirrored by 9 - 5 = 4 and 9 - 4 = 5.

The addition facts can be presented in a table square. There is an extra addition facts table square at the back of the book and also there are two blank table squares for you to fill in to mark your progress.

Table of addition facts

+	0	1	2	3	4	5	6	7	8	9	10
0	0	1	2	3	4	5	6	7	8	9	10
1	1	2	3	4	5	6	7	8	9	10	11
2	2	3	4	5	6	7	8	9	10	11	12
3	3	4	5	6	7	8	9	10	11	12	13
4	4	5	6	7	8	9	10	11	12	13	14
5	5	6	7	8	9	10	11	12	13	14	15
6	6	7	8	9	10	11	12	13	14	15	16
7	7	8	9	10	11	12	13	14	15	16	17
8	8	9	10	11	12	13	14	15	16	17	18
9	9	10	11	12	13	14	15	16	17	18	19
10	10	11	12	13	14	15	16	17	18	19	20

Words which mean
ADD

Total, Sum, Plus
More than, And,
Put Together

but Beware!
see page 5

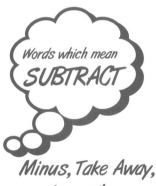

Words which mean
SUBTRACT

Minus, Take Away,
Less Than,
Difference

but Beware!
see page 6

The interchange of the two numbers being added *(e.g. 5+7 and 7+5)* does not affect the total of the two numbers.
This characteristic of addition is called the *COMMUTATIVE* property.

But....

Subtraction facts are NOT commutative. For example
8-3=5,
but
5-8=-3 (minus 3)

Strategies for learning addition and subtraction facts.

The idea is to remember some facts and have easy ways of working out the other facts. The methods are;

counting on (1 and 2)
understanding 0
adding on 10
adding on 9
using number bonds for 10
using doubles (eg 3 + 3)

These strategies will also help your understanding of numbers.

Counting on 1 and 2. Subtracting 1 and 2.

It is very quick to finger count on 1 or 2. Always add on the small number to the bigger number, for example with 2 + 8, add 2 onto the 8.........counting 9, **10**.

It is also quick to finger count back to subtract 1 or 2 or to finger count from the lower number to the target number, for example 10 - 8 is counted as 2 numbers on from 8, counting 9, 10.

Practise and aim to be accurate and quick (being quick, not rushed, can help your memory cope better with the rest of the sum).

Remember that each addition fact is two facts (except 1 + 1, 2 + 2 etc)

so   5 + 1   and   1 + 5   both make 6

5 + 1 = 6   and   1 + 5 = 6

ADDING AND SUBTRACTING 1

0 + 1 = 1	1 + 0 = 1	1 - 1 = 0
1 + 1 = 2	1 + 1 = 2	2 - 1 = 1
2 + 1 = 3	1 + 2 = 3	3 - 1 = 2
3 + 1 = 4	1 + 3 = 4	4 - 1 = 3
4 + 1 = 5	1 + 4 = 5	5 - 1 = 4

$5 + 1 = 6$	$1 + 5 = 6$	$6 - 1 = 5$
$6 + 1 = 7$	$1 + 6 = 7$	$7 - 1 = 6$
$7 + 1 = 8$	$1 + 7 = 8$	$8 - 1 = 7$
$8 + 1 = 9$	$1 + 8 = 9$	$9 - 1 = 8$
$9 + 1 = 10$	$1 + 9 = 10$	$10 - 1 = 9$

ADDING AND SUBTRACTING 2

$0 + 2 = 2$	$2 + 0 = 2$	$2 - 2 = 0$
$1 + 2 = 3$	$2 + 1 = 3$	$3 - 2 = 1$
$2 + 2 = 4$	$2 + 2 = 4$	$4 - 2 = 2$
$3 + 2 = 5$	$2 + 3 = 5$	$5 - 2 = 3$
$4 + 2 = 6$	$2 + 4 = 6$	$6 - 2 = 4$
$5 + 2 = 7$	$2 + 5 = 7$	$7 - 2 = 5$
$6 + 2 = 8$	$2 + 6 = 8$	$8 - 2 = 6$
$7 + 2 = 9$	$2 + 7 = 9$	$9 - 2 = 7$
$8 + 2 = 10$	$2 + 8 = 10$	$10 - 2 = 8$
$9 + 2 = 11$	$2 + 9 = 11$	$11 - 2 = 9$
$10 + 2 = 12$	$2 + 10 = 12$	$12 - 2 = 10$

You have mastered 40 addition facts.........
81 to go!.........

Shade in these facts on an addition square. Use different colours for each set of facts.

UNDERSTANDING ZERO

0 or zero is used to represent the idea of nothing.

One of the ways it is used to represent nothing is in the way we write numbers.......

Counting from 1 to 9 takes you through all the unit digits

1 2 3 4 5 6 7 8 9

Beware!

*Words for **add** can also be used in questions which can be done by* subtraction.
For example:
"What number added to 56 gives 78?"
could be done by the subtraction sum
78-56=22

Did You Know?...

...that the Romans had no zero, because they could see no point in having a symbol for nothing. How can you represent nothing with something? So they ignored it!

5

a 1p coin is equivalent to 1 unit

a 10p coin is equivalent to 1 ten

a £1 coin is equivalent to 1 hundred

Beware. . .

. . . words that are used for subtraction could also mean add, for example, "The difference between two numbers is 34. The smaller number is 52. What is the other number?" could be done as 34+52=86.

The next number in this sequence is ten, 10, which has two digits, a 1 and a 0.

One of the early experiences of zero for most people is its use with the tens, that is

ten, 10, twenty, 20, thirty, 30, forty, 40, fifty, 50, sixty, 60, seventy, 70, eighty, 80, ninety, 90.

In each of these tens numbers the zero, 0, is used
to tell us that there are no units
and to push the tens digit into the place value position for tens.

PLACE VALUE

In the number 10, the 1 and 0 are in the right order to be ten. The 0 is in the *place* which means *units* and the 1 is in the *place* which means *tens*. So the *place value* of 0 is *zero units* and the *place value* of 1 is *one ten*.

Another example **60**

six tens   *zero units*

The next number after 60 is 61. The 6 still means *6 tens*. The 1 represents *1 unit*..

Another example, 537, **537**

a hundred place value has been introduced (5)

5 hundreds   *3 tens*   *7 units*

and another, 704,
with 704, the zero means there are no tens. The zero pushes the 7 into the hundreds place.

704

7 hundreds   *0 tens*   *4 units*

If you did not use the zero 704 would be 74 (seventy four), so one of zero's important uses is to push other digits into their correct place value.

ADDING AND SUBTRACTING ZERO

Zero acts as **nothing** when it is added or subtracted from another number.

Adding nothing and subtracting nothing to a number does not change the number. For example,

$$5 + 0 = 5 \qquad 5 - 0 = 5$$

$$10 + 0 = 10 \qquad 10 - 0 = 10$$

This means that the zero facts are easy.

*Digits
and
Numbers. . .*

ADDING AND SUBTRACTING 0

$0 + 0 = 0$	$0 + 0 = 0$	$0 - 0 = 0$
$0 + 1 = 1$	$1 + 0 = 1$	$1 - 0 = 1$
$0 + 2 = 2$	$2 + 0 = 2$	$2 - 0 = 2$
$0 + 3 = 3$	$3 + 0 = 3$	$3 - 0 = 3$
$0 + 4 = 4$	$4 + 0 = 4$	$4 - 0 = 4$
$0 + 5 = 5$	$5 + 0 = 5$	$5 - 0 = 5$
$0 + 6 = 6$	$6 + 0 = 6$	$6 - 0 = 6$
$0 + 7 = 7$	$7 + 0 = 7$	$7 - 0 = 7$
$0 + 8 = 8$	$8 + 0 = 8$	$8 - 0 = 8$
$0 + 9 = 9$	$9 + 0 = 9$	$9 - 0 = 9$
$0 + 10 = 10$	$10 + 0 = 10$	$10 - 0 = 10$

*. . a **DIGIT** is one of 0,1,2,3,4,5,6,7,8 or 9. . .*

*. . a **NUMBER** is made up of one or more digits, for example 63 or 941.*

Write these numbers in digits

Four thousand, six hundred and thirty two

....

Two thousand and one

....

Two thousand and fifty one

....

Six hundred and three

....

Coins are used to help give you a picture of what the numbers are doing. Use the coins and numbers at the same time so that you see the connections at all times.

Once you have learned to add 0, 1 and 2, you have learned 57 addition facts (64 to go) and 33 subtraction facts.

Shade in an addition number square to show your progress.

ADDING ON 10. SUBTRACTING 10

Ten has two digits, a 1 and a 0. The zero means there a no units. This means that adding units is easy..... it goe straight into the unit place, unchanged.

Look at the pattern............

For example,

$10 + 6 = 16$ $10 + 3 = 13$ $10 + 9 = 19$ $10 + 2 = 12$

It also makes easy subtractions

$16 - 6 = 10$ $13 - 3 = 10$ $19 - 9 = 10$ $12 - 2 = 1($

Try this with coins. Use 1p and 10p coins.

For example; 10 + 6

The 10p coin represents 1 ten and 0 units, so adding si: 1p coins makes 1 ten and 6 units, that is 16p.

ADDING 10

0 + **10** = 10	**10** + 0 = 10
1 + **10** = 11	**10** + 1 = 11
2 + **10** = 12	**10** + 2 = 12
3 + **10** = 13	**10** + 3 = 13
4 + **10** = 14	**10** + 4 = 14
5 + **10** = 15	**10** + 5 = 15
6 + **10** = 16	**10** + 6 = 16
7 + **10** = 17	**10** + 7 = 17
8 + **10** = 18	**10** + 8 = 18
9 + **10** = 19	**10** + 9 = 19
10 + **10** = 20	**10** + 10 = 20

SUBTRACTING 10

10 - **10** = 0
11 - **10** = 1
12 - **10** = 2
13 - **10** = 3
14 - **10** = 4
15 - **10** = 5
16 - **10** = 6
17 - **10** = 7
18 - **10** = 8
19 - **10** = 9
20 - **10** = 10

The addition facts for 10 give you 15 'new' facts.

49 addition facts to go.

Use another colour to shade in the 10 facts on your addition square.

Try This!

If you want to know more about self voice echo, Dr. Colin Lane is the UK's top expert. He can be contacted at ARROW,

01278 446261

Try recording some of these addition and subtraction facts on audio tape and then playing them back, preferably through headphones, while looking at the written version.

If you say them at the same time, then you are using eyes, ears and voice to push each fact into your memory. Try using the PLAY and REWIND buttons to keep repeating the fact back, one time after another.

SELF VOICE ECHO can be a very powerful learning idea.

DOUBLES

It is useful if the doubles (eg 3 + 3) can be learned.

Note that the answers to the doubles **addition** facts are all **even numbers**.

0 + 0 = 0	0 - 0 = 0
1 + 1 = 2	2 - 1 = 1
2 + 2 = 4	4 - 2 = 2
3 + 3 = 6	6 - 3 = 3
4 + 4 = 8	8 - 4 = 4
5 + 5 = 10	10 - 5 = 5
6 + 6 = 12	12 - 6 = 6
7 + 7 = 14	14 - 7 = 7
8 + 8 = 16	16 - 8 = 8
9 + 9 = 18	18 - 9 = 9
10+10 = 20	20 - 10 = 10

This gives 7 new facts, 42 to go.
Shade in these facts on a number square to show your progress.

IMAGES

Try some images to help fix these basic facts in your memory. Try them out and see which one is best for you.

 FINGERS

There are 10 fingers (thumbs count as fingers in maths). You can use each hand as a reminder that 5 + 5 = 10, that is 5 fingers on each hand, 10 altogether.

You can also use your 10 fingers as tallies for counting up in 2's............

2, 4, 6, 8, 10, 12, 14, 16, 18, 20

Even and *Odd* numbers...
even numbers can be
divided (split up) into two
equal, whole number
amounts.
For example 16=8+8.

*...Odd numbers divide
(split up) into two whole
numbers which are not
equal and differ by one.*
For example 13=7+6.

NUMBER LINE

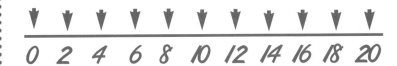

COINS

Use 2p coins to count, each coin counts 2

2   4   6   8   10

At this stage you could trade the five 2p coins for one 10p

10p + 2p

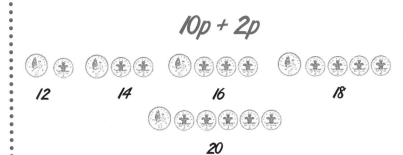

12   14   16   18

20

or you could just count through in two rows

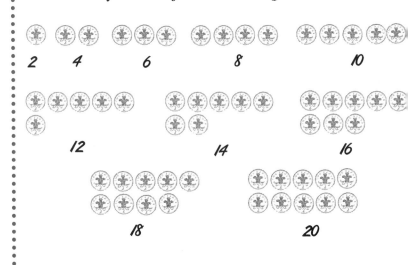

2   4   6   8   10

12   14   16

18   20

BUILDING ON THE DOUBLES

1. Doubles plus 1

Set up the example $4 + 4$ in coins

  $+$ $4 + 4 = 8$

Adding in 1 more coin will take the answer to 9
$(8 + 1 = 9)$. The extra coin may be added to the first 4 or the second 4 to give two more facts.

$5 + 4 = 9$

$4 + 5 = 9$

This can be done with all the doubles, for example

$6 + 6 = 12$

Add 1 to take the answer to 13 $(12 + 1 = 13)$

$7 + 6 = 13$

$6 + 7 = 13$

Note that the answers to the addition facts for doubles plus 1 are all **odd numbers.**

DOUBLES PLUS 1

$1 + 1 = 2$	$1 + 2 = 3$	$2 + 1 = 3$
$2 + 2 = 4$	$2 + 3 = 5$	$3 + 2 = 5$
$3 + 3 = 6$	$3 + 4 = 7$	$4 + 3 = 7$
$4 + 4 = 8$	$4 + 5 = 9$	$5 + 4 = 9$
$5 + 5 = 10$	$5 + 6 = 11$	$6 + 5 = 11$
$6 + 6 = 12$	$6 + 7 = 13$	$7 + 6 = 13$
$7 + 7 = 14$	$7 + 8 = 15$	$8 + 7 = 15$
$8 + 8 = 16$	$8 + 9 = 17$	$9 + 8 = 17$
$9 + 9 = 18$	$9 + 10 = 19$	$10 + 9 = 19$

$6 + 6 = 12$

$+$

$=$

$6 + 7 = 13$

$+$

$=$

13

Look at the patterns down each column of answers. The answers to the doubles is the sequence of even numbers. The answers to the doubles plus one is the sequence of odd numbers. Using the coins to work out these facts gives the reason for this (even number plus even number gives an even number.........odd number plus even number gives an odd number).

Shade in these facts on a new addition square and look at the pattern. Shade in the doubles facts (in a different colour). Look at the pattern.

The equivalent subtraction facts are;

3 - 1 = 2	3 - 2 = 1
5 - 2 = 3	5 - 3 = 2
7 - 3 = 4	7 - 4 = 3
9 - 4 = 5	9 - 5 = 4
11 - 5 = 6	11 - 6 = 5
13 - 6 = 7	13 - 7 = 6
15 - 7 = 8	15 - 8 = 7
17 - 8 = 9	17 - 9 = 8
19 - 9 = 10	19 - 10 = 9

Look at the patterns down each column. There are sequences in each column.

It may help to remember that each starting number is a double plus 1. It often helps to remember how **numbers can be broken down**. In these examples each starting number breaks down into a double plus 1. For example, 17 breaks down into 8 + 8 + 1 and 9 breaks down into 4 + 4 + 1.

Try setting out some of these examples in coins

9 as 5 and 4   9 as 4 and 4 plus 1

2. SHARING DOUBLES

Set up the example of 4 + 4 in coins

$4 + 4 = 8$

Now move 1 coin over

= 8 coins

= 8 coins

There are still 8 coins, but $4 + 4 = 8$ has become
$3 + 5 = 8$.

A coin can also be moved to make $4 + 4 = 8$
become $5 + 3 = 8$

Each double fact can become two shared double facts.

Try the others with coins

SHARED DOUBLES

$2 + 2 = 4$	$1 + 3 = 4$	$3 + 1 = 4$
$3 + 3 = 6$	$2 + 4 = 6$	$4 + 2 = 6$

A milkman has only a 3 litre jug and a 5 litre jug to measure out his milk. He needs to give a customer 1 litre. How can he use his jugs to measure 1 litre without spilling any milk?

Make up a similar problem with two different jugs.

$$4+4=8 \qquad 3+5=8 \qquad 5+3=8$$

$$5+5=10 \qquad 4+6=10 \qquad 6+4=10$$

$$6+6=12 \qquad 5+7=12 \qquad 7+5=12$$

$$7+7=14 \qquad 6+8=14 \qquad 8+6=14$$

$$8+8=16 \qquad 7+9=16 \qquad 9+7=16$$

$$9+9=18 \qquad 8+10=18 \qquad 10+8=18$$

Note that the 'shared' numbers are one more and one less than the double number, so for **6** the shared numbers are 7 (6+1) and 5 (6-1).

Shade in these facts on your (doubles) number square.

Look at each pattern for the doubles, doubles plus 1 and shared doubles.

The doubles plus and minus 1 and the shared doubles have given you 22 new facts. *20 to go.*

Shade in these facts on your number square

Adding on 9

9 is a lovely example to show how finger counting is slow and inefficient.
Some numbers are easier to use than others. These easier numbers can be used to help you work with harder numbers. 9 can be difficult but if you use 10 to help, 9 becomes very easy.

Remember that **9 is 1 less than 10,
so an easy way to add 9 is to add 10 and take off 1.**

Look at some examples;

9 + 8.
 Treat the 9 as though it was 10
10 + 8 = 18
 Then take off 1 from 18 to give the answer
9 + 8 = 17

Two quick (easier) steps take the place of one long (harder) step.

9 + 6   is done as   10 + 6 - 1

10 + 6 = 16   then   16 - 1 = **15**

Try this game;

Person B has 21 one pence coins and 4 ten pence coins. Person A asks person B to give him 9p. Usually person B counts out 9 one pence coins. Person A asks for another 9p and person B again counts out 9 one pence coins. Person A asks for a third 9p, but B only has 3 one pence coins left. B can solve this problem by giving A one 10p coin and taking one 1p coin back from A. This is, of course, an example of 10 - 1 = 9.

ADDING 9

In each case the answer for adding 10 has been printed in **outline** next to the answer for adding 9.

$0 + 9 = 9$	**10**		$9 + 0 = 9$	**10**
$1 + 9 = 10$	**11**		$9 + 1 = 10$	**11**
$2 + 9 = 11$	**12**		$9 + 2 = 11$	**12**
$3 + 9 = 12$	**13**		$9 + 3 = 12$	**13**
$4 + 9 = 13$	**14**		$9 + 4 = 13$	**14**
$5 + 9 = 14$	**15**		$9 + 5 = 14$	**15**
$6 + 9 = 15$	**16**		$9 + 6 = 15$	**16**
$7 + 9 = 16$	**17**		$9 + 7 = 16$	**17**
$8 + 9 = 17$	**18**		$9 + 8 = 17$	**18**
$9 + 9 = 18$	**19**		$9 + 9 = 18$	**19**
$10 + 9 = 19$	**20**		$9 + 10 = 19$	**20**

Other uses of this strategy

This strategy of adding 10 and taking away 1 is useful for adding 9 to any number.

For example;

$56 + 9$ is done as $56 + 10 = 66$, then take off 1 to give the answer 65

$$56 + 9 = 65$$

It is also useful in those shops which use prices such as £7.99, which is £8.00 minus 1p. Adding £3.99 + £5.99 + £2.99 becomes £4 + £6 + £3 minus 3p, that is £13 minus 3p, an answer of £12.97. (see also page 68)

It can also be used for working out 9 times table facts (see the book, 'What to do when you can't learn the times tables' also published by Egon).

When you can do these addition facts for 9, you have learned 8 more new facts,

12 to go.

Shade in these facts on your number square.

Try this with cards!

Take a pack of playing cards. Take out all the picture cards. This leaves you with four sets of cards from 1 to 10. Shuffle them and take two out at a time, for extra practise examples in adding.

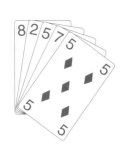

Number bonds for 10

These are the pairs of numbers which add together to make 10, for example

$$3 + 7 = 10.$$

They are a family of important and useful facts. There are some ways to help remember them based on how they relate.

1. Look at all your 10 fingers, a total of 10. An obvious sum is $5 + 5 = 10$, 5 fingers on one hand and 5 fingers on the other hand.

10 fingers could also be separated as

1 finger and 9 fingers,

then 2 fingers and 8 fingers

then 3 fingers and 7 fingers

then 4 fingers and 6 fingers

then 5 fingers and 5 fingers

then 6 fingers and 4 fingers

(you are now taking the complementary facts)

then 7 fingers and 3 fingers $(3 + 7)$

then 8 fingers and 2 fingers $(2 + 8)$

then 9 fingers and 1 finger $(1 + 9)$

This is a really good example of the connection between addition and subtraction facts. We started by looking at how 10 (fingers) could separate into two numbers, for example, if we have 2 fingers separated from 10 fingers, this leaves 8 fingers $10 - 2 = 8$. We then used this separation of 10 as an addition fact $8 + 2 = 10$.

Number bonds for 10 can also be practised with coins. Set up 10 coins like this

5+5=10

Now move 1 coin

4+6=10

Move 1 more coin

3+7=10

Do this three more times to show 2+8=10, 1+9=10, 0+10=10, Then return to the 5+5 arrangement and move coins to show 6+4=10, 7+3=10, etc.

2. Use a stack of 10 Lego bricks.
The stack of 10 can be separated as

9 + 1
8 + 2
7 + 3
6 + 4
5 + 5
4 + 6
3 + 7
2 + 8
1 + 9

3. This picture sometimes helps

$$9\ 8\ 7\ 6\ 5\ 4\ 3\ 2\ 1$$
$$1\ 2\ 3\ 4\ 5\ 6\ 7\ 8\ 9$$

NUMBER BONDS FOR 10

0 + 10 = 10	10 + 0 = 10
1 + 9 = 10	9 + 1 = 10
2 + 8 = 10	8 + 2 = 10
3 + 7 = 10	7 + 3 = 10
4 + 6 = 10	6 + 4 = 10
5 + 5 = 10	5 + 5 = 10
6 + 4 = 10	4 + 6 = 10
7 + 3 = 10	3 + 7 = 10
8 + 2 = 10	2 + 8 = 10
9 + 1 = 10	1 + 9 = 10
10 + 0 = 10	0 + 10 = 10

The equivalent subtraction facts are;

$$10 - 0 = 10$$
$$10 - 1 = 9$$
$$10 - 2 = 8$$
$$10 - 3 = 7$$
$$10 - 4 = 6$$
$$10 - 5 = 5$$
$$10 - 6 = 4$$
$$10 - 7 = 3$$
$$10 - 8 = 2$$
$$10 - 9 = 1$$
$$10 - 10 = 0$$

Building on the number bonds for 10

1. Adding 1   (number bonds for 11)
We extended the doubles facts by adding 1. We can do this with the number bonds for 10. This gives us number bonds for 10 + 1 which is 11.
For example;

$6 + 4 = 10$ so $6 + 5 = 11$ and $7 + 4 = 11$

Try illustrating this by using coins. Set up two lots of 10 coins like this

$$6 + 4 = 10$$

$$5 + 5 = 10$$

Add one coin to each group, making

$$6 + 5 = 11$$

$$5 + 6 = 11$$

Try setting up some number pyramids to practise addition. The pyramid starts at the bottom. Adjacent numbers are added to make a number on the next row up. A worked example is done for you.

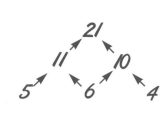

Try!

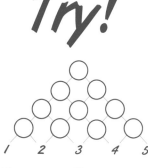

Make some others using numbers you choose

1 + 10 = 11	10 + 1 = 11
2 + 9 = 11	9 + 2 = 11
3 + 8 = 11	8 + 3 = 11
4 + 7 = 11	7 + 4 = 11
5 + 6 = 11	6 + 5 = 11
6 + 5 = 11	5 + 6 = 11
7 + 4 = 11	4 + 7 = 11
8 + 3 = 11	3 + 8 = 11
9 + 2 = 11	2 + 9 = 11
10 + 1 = 11	1 + 10 = 11

and the subtraction facts.......

11 - 10 = 1

11 - 9 = 2

11 - 8 = 3

11 - 7 = 4

11 - 6 = 5

11 - 5 = 6

11 - 4 = 7

11 - 3 = 8

11 - 2 = 9

11 - 1 = 10

11 - 0 = 11

2. Subtracting 1   (number bonds for 9)

Taking off 1 from the number bonds for 10 creates the
number bonds for 9.

0 + 9 = 9	9 + 0 = 9
1 + 8 = 9	8 + 1 = 9
2 + 7 = 9	7 + 2 = 9
3 + 6 = 9	6 + 3 = 9
4 + 5 = 9	5 + 4 = 9
5 + 4 = 9	4 + 5 = 9
6 + 3 = 9	3 + 6 = 9
7 + 2 = 9	2 + 7 = 9
8 + 1 = 9	1 + 8 = 9
0 + 9 = 9	0 + 9 = 9

The subtraction facts are;

9 - 0 = 9	9 - 9 = 0
9 - 1 = 8	10 - 9 = 1
9 - 2 = 7	11 - 9 = 2
9 - 3 = 6	12 - 9 = 3
9 - 4 = 5	13 - 9 = 4
9 - 5 = 4	14 - 9 = 5
9 - 6 = 3	15 - 9 = 6
9 - 7 = 2	16 - 9 = 7
9 - 8 = 1	17 - 9 = 8
9 - 9 = 0	18 - 9 = 9
	19 - 9 = 10

The last four facts are

$$8 + 4 = 12 \qquad\qquad 4 + 8 = 12$$
$$8 + 5 = 13 \qquad\qquad 5 + 8 = 13$$

and as subtraction

$$12 - 4 = 8 \qquad\qquad 12 - 8 = 4$$
$$13 - 5 = 8 \qquad\qquad 13 - 8 = 5$$

FINAL REMINDER NOTE ON BASIC ADDITION AND SUBTRACTION FACTS

It does not matter which number you ADD to which, the answer is the same.

For example $\qquad 6 + 7 = 13 \qquad\qquad 7 + 6 = 13$

It DOES matter which number you SUBTRACT from which, the answer will NOT be the same.

For example $\qquad 9 - 3 = 6 \qquad\qquad 3 - 9 = -6$

$$(minus\ 6)$$

STUDY SKILLS

Now that you have seen how the addition and subtraction facts relate and build together you have to use the information to help your memory and to help you understand numbers and arithmetic.

The basic advice is $\qquad$ *PRACTISE*

Any skill whether it is soccer, playing the violin or doing mathematics needs regular practice
........little and often usually works best.

Vary the practice to give different input and help maintain interest. For example, sometimes write down work, sometimes talk it through to yourself or someone else. Use money to help picture what is happening and make the processes clearer.
(Understanding helps memory).
These materials also make learning multi-sensory, that is you are putting the information into your brain using several senses, vision, hearing, speech and movement. These inputs should help fix the information in the brain.

Look around and see where maths comes into your life.

Don't be passive! Work out your change in shops, etc. Use estimates to check bills. Estimate journey times. Learn to be confident with numbers!

Before we take a careful look at addition and subtraction problems, you have to learn about a process used in both *....TRADING*

Trading suggests a fair exchange. In this case the ten 1p coins are traded for a 10p coin which is, of course, the same value. The same applies to the trade of a 10p coin for ten 1p coins

Trading is the process of exchanging (trading);
10 units into 1 ten   e.g. 10 one pence coins for 1 ten pence coin

and
1 ten into 10 units   e.g. 1 ten pence coin for 10 one pence coins

and
10 tens into 1 hundred   e.g. 10 ten pence coins for 1 pound coin (100 pence)

and
1 hundred into 10 tens   e.g. 1 pound coin (100 pence) for 10 ten pence coins

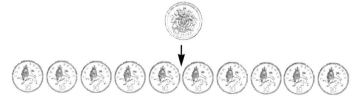

Trading is used in addition and subtraction sums.

Consider *adding* 7 and 9

$$7 + 9 = 16$$

The answer is sixteen, that is one ten and six units.

If we use coins to show what happens;

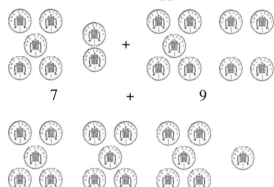

There are many trading games you can play to help you understand this procedure. Set a target sum of money, for example £2.35 Use the playing cards (see page 18) and draw one at a time. Take that number of coins from a 'bank' of 1p and 10p coins. As soon as you go over nine 1p coins, trade for 10p and as soon as you get over nine 10p coins trade for £1. The first person to reach the target amount wins (you could opt to take two cards each time).

We can trade 10 one pence coins for 1 ten pence coin

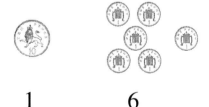

Now consider 16 minus 9

$$16 - 9 = 7$$

If we start where we just ended the addition sum, that is with 16 as

We do not have enough one pence coins to take nine away. To obtain some more one pence coins we trade the 1 ten pence coin for 10 one pence coins. This gives sixteen one pence coins.

Now take away (subtract) 9, leaving 7.

$$16 - 9 = 7$$

This means that we can write numbers in a way that shows trading has been used, usually for subtraction purposes. For example; with the subtraction *72 - 48* the units subtraction has to take 8 from 2. Trading 1 ten for 10 units (in the 72) changes 72 from 7 tens and 2 units to 6 tens and 12 units.

This gives us two versions of 72......that is added together they both make 72

$$72 \quad = \quad 70 + 2$$
$$72 \quad = \quad 60 + 12$$

We can show this with coins...........

70 + 2

60 + 12

This also works with tens.............

$$437 \quad = \quad 400 + 30 + 7$$
$$437 \quad = \quad 300 + 130 + 7$$

Use £1, 10p and 1p coins to show different ways of having the same sum of money. For Example £4.23 could be..
4x£1 + 2x10p + 3x1p
or.... 3x£1 + 12x10p + 3x1p

ADDING   8 + 7 = 15

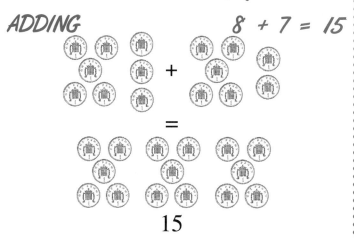

+

=

15

trade 10 one pence coins   for 1 ten pence coin

SUBTRACTING   15 - 8 = 7

trade 1 ten pence coin for 10 one pence coins

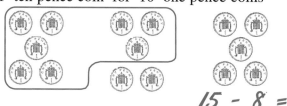

15 - 8 = 7

Also remember;

$58 = 50 + 8$ and $58 = 40 + 18$

$864 = 800 + 60 + 4$ and $864 = 700 + 160 + 4$

ADDING AND SUBTRACTING.......WRITTEN METHODS

This section will explain how to add and subtract when you have paper and a pen available. If you now know your basic facts, that will help. If you do not, you will be a little slower and you should take just a little more care. The practice will be beneficial.

Main Points

1. Adding and subtracting work to the same procedure - one forward and one reverse.
2. Both procedures use "trading" (see page 26).
3. When coins are used to show what is happening, they follow exactly the same steps as the written method.
4. You need to remember what place values are (units, tens, hundreds, etc).

We will start with a basic example and then build in trading skills to use in 'harder' examples. In each case, the example will be presented in three ways;
1. money
2. place value columns
3. numbers on their own
Use the presentation which supports your understanding. You will probably start with the money and move to the numbers as your skill improves. Take time to understand what you are doing.
In order to show that addition and subtraction are the same process in opposite directions, each example adds two numbers and then subtracts to arrive back at the start. Please work through the examples.....they are set out to help you to understand the two processes.

Adding with no trading

26 + 43

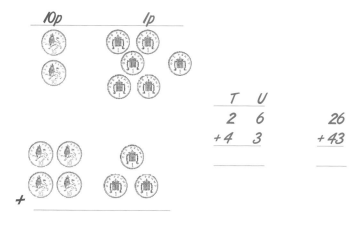

Try each example with the coins first. Write the relevant numbers as you move the coins

1. Using the coins.
Add together the one pence coins. Add three one pence coins to six one pence coins to make nine one pence coins. The total for the one pence / units column is **9**.

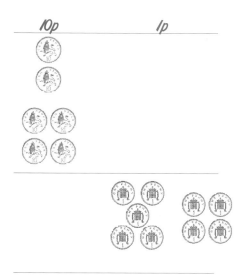

Now add together the ten pence coins. Add two ten pence coins to four ten pence coins to make six ten pence coins. The total for the ten pence / tens column is **6**.

31

The answer is 69.

2. Using place value columns.
Add together the numbers in the units (U) column.
6 + 3 = 9. Write **9** in the units column on the answer line.

$$
\begin{array}{r r}
T & U \\
2 & 6 \\
+\ 4 & 3 \\
\hline
 & 9 \\
\end{array}
$$

Add together the numbers in the tens (T) column.
2 + 4 = 6. Write **6** in the tens column on the answer line.

$$
\begin{array}{r r}
T & U \\
2 & 6 \\
+\ 4 & 3 \\
\hline
6 & 9 \\
\end{array}
$$

The answer is 69.

3. Using numbers on their own.

Add together the units numbers. 6 + 3 = 9. Write **9** in the units place of the answer line.

$$
\begin{array}{r}
2\ 6 \\
+4\ 3 \\
\hline
?\ 9 \\
\end{array}
$$

Add together the tens numbers. $2 + 4 = 6$. Write **6** in the tens place of the answer line.

$$
\begin{array}{r}
2\ 6 \\
+4\ 3 \\
\hline
6\ 9 \\
\end{array}
$$

The answer is 69.

Review
In this addition you start in the units column.
You add the two numbers in the units column together.
The number which is the total from this addition is written in the units column on the answer line.
You then add together the numbers in the tens column and write this number in the tens column on the answer line.

Subtracting with no trading

69 - 26   (We shall reverse the addition example)

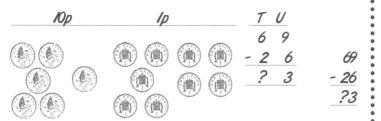

$$
\begin{array}{cc}
T & U \\
6 & 9 \\
-\ 2 & 6 \\
\hline
? & 3 \\
\end{array}
\qquad
\begin{array}{r}
69 \\
-\ 26 \\
\hline
?3 \\
\end{array}
$$

1. Using the coins.
Take away 6 one pence coins (units), leaving 3 one pence coins. The answer in the one pence / units column is **3** coins.

33

Now take away 2 ten pence coins (tens), leaving 4 ten pence coins. The answer in the ten pence / tens column is **4** coins.

$$
\begin{array}{r}
6\ 9 \\
-\ 2\ 6 \\
\hline
4\ 3
\end{array}
$$

The final answer is 43.

2. Using place value columns.
The top number is 69. The number you are taking away from this is 26. Start in the units (U) column. 9 - 6 = 3. Write **3** in the units column on the answer line.

T	U
6	9
- 2	6
	3

Move to the tens (T) column and subtract from the top number. 6 - 2 = 4. Write **4** in the tens column on the answer line.

T	U
6	9
- 2	6
4	3

The answer is 43.

Review.
In this subtraction you start in the **units** column.
You take away the number in the lower line from the number on the top line and write the answer underneath on the answer line and in the **units** column.
You then take away the **tens** numbers, the lower line from the number on the top line and write the answer underneath on the answer line and in the **tens** column.

Practise exercise A.

1a. 45 + 31   *1b.* 76 - 45

2a. 22 + 75   *2b.* 97 - 22

(Check your answers to questions 1a, 1b, 2a and 2b (page 36) before you try any more. If you are wrong, read the section again and work through the examples again, using coins to help understanding).

3a.　54 + 34　　　　3b.　88 - 34

4a.　41 + 23　　　　4b.　64 - 23

For examples 5 to 10, you should look carefully at both numbers and estimate an answer as a back-up to the accurate procedure.

5.　57 + 32　　　　6.　77 - 47

7.　12 + 53　　　　8.　65 - 34

9.　86 - 55　　　　10.　42 + 42

answers on page 37

Adding with trading in the units / tens columns.

In these examples, when the two numbers in the units column are added they will total 10 or more. This will result in trading units for tens (see page 26).

36 + 57

10p	1p		T	U	
			3	6	36
		+	5	7	+ 57
			?	3	? 3

+ _____

1. Using the coins

Add together the one pence coins. Add 6 one pence coins to 7 one pence coins to make 13 one pence coins (note how the arrangement of the one pence coins makes this addition easier.....6 is set out as 5 + 1.... 7 is set out as 5 + 2.... the addition is 5 + 5 = 10 plus 1 + 2 =3, making 13).

Now *TRADE* 10 one pence coins for 1 ten pence coin, leaving 3 one pence coins (units). The total for the one pence / units column is **3**. Put the traded ten pence coin in the tens column.

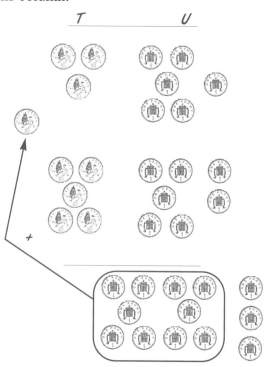

Now add the ten pence coins. Add 3 ten pence coins to 5 ten pence coins plus 1 ten pence (traded) coin to make 9 ten pence coins. The total for the ten pence / units column is **9**.

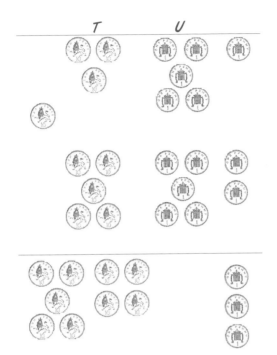

The answer is **93.**

2. Using place value columns
Add together the numbers in the units (U) column.
6 + 7 = 13. Thirteen is 3 units and 1 ten. Write **3** in the units column on the answer line and write **1** (actually 1 ten) at the top of the tens (T) column.

```
      T   U
      3'  6
    + 5   7
    ─────────
          3
```

Add together the numbers in the tens (T) column.
3 + 5 + 1 = 9. Write **9** in the tens column on the answer line.

```
      T   U
      3'  6
    + 5   7
    ─────────
      9   3
```

The answer is **93.**

Answers to practise exercise A, questions 3 to 10
3a. 88 3b. 54 4a. 64 4b. 41
5. 89 6. 30 7. 65
8. 31 9. 31 10. 84

3. Using numbers on their own.

Start in the units column and add together the unit numbers......6 + 7 = 13. Write the **3** units in the units column on the answer line. Write the **1** (actually 1 ten) above the 3 at the top of the tens column.

$$
\begin{array}{r}
1 \\
3\,\mathbf{6} \\
+5\,\mathbf{7} \\
\hline
\mathbf{3} \\
\end{array}
$$

Add the numbers in the tens column....3 + 5 + 1 = 9. Write **9** in the tens column on the number line.

$$
\begin{array}{r}
1 \\
3\,6 \\
+5\,7 \\
\hline
\mathbf{9}\,3 \\
\end{array}
$$

The answer is **93.**

Subtraction with trading in the units / tens columns

93 - 57

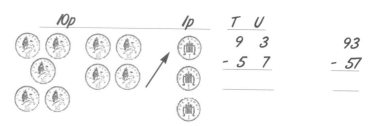

1. Using the coins

Start with the one pence coins. You need to subtract 7 coins, but you only have 3, so you must **TRADE.** Take one ten pence coin from the 9 in the tens column and trade it for 10 one pence coins. (This leaves 8 ten pence coins).

10p   1p

You now have 13 one pence coins and can subtract 7.........13 - 7 = 6. The answer in the one pence / units column is **6**.

Now move to the ten pence coins. There are 8 left and you must subtract 5................

8 - 5 = 3. The answer in the ten pence / tens column is **3**. The answer is **36**.

2. Using place value columns

You have 3 in the upper position number in the units column. You need to subtract 7 from this 3 and since 3 is smaller than 7, you must **TRADE.** Take one ten from the 9 (tens) in the tens (T) column, leaving 8 and transfer this ten into the units (U) column to make 3 units up to 13.

Your 93 now looks like this $\cancel{9}\,8$ 13

You can now subtract 7 from 13..........13 - 7 = 6. Write **6** on the answer line in the units column. Now move to the tens (T) column. You have to subtract 5 from 8......8 - 5 = 3. Write **3** on the answer line in the tens column.
The answer is **36**.

$$
\begin{array}{cc}
T & U \\
\hline
\cancel{9}8 & {}^{1}3 \\
-5 & 7 \\
\hline
3 & 6
\end{array}
$$

3. Using numbers on their own

$$
\begin{array}{c}
\cancel{9}8\ {}^{1}3 \\
-5\ 7 \\
\hline
3\ 6
\end{array}
$$

Practise exercise B.

1a. 39 + 43	*1b. 82 - 39*
2a. 55 + 28	*2b. 83 - 55*

(Check your answers to these examples (page 42) before trying the rest. If you are wrong, read the section again and work through the examples again.)

3.	*28 + 34*	*4.*	*67 - 39*
5.	*75 + 17*	*6.*	*51 - 46*
7.	*34 + 56*	*8.*	*91 - 54*
9.	*86 - 47*	*10.*	*87 + 8*
11.	*72 - 53*	*12.*	*67 - 28*

(answers on page 44)

A palindromic number reads the same forwards and backwards, for example 9449 when reversed is still 9449. If you add 56 to 65 (56 reversed) you get 121 which is palindromic. Can you find some other two digit numbers which make a palindromic number by this process?

Adding with trading in both the units / tens and tens / hundreds columns

67 + 84

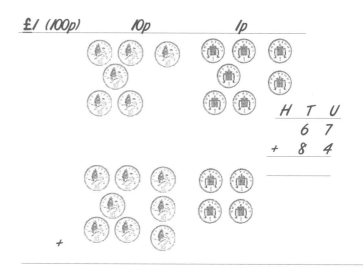

£1 (100p)   10p   1p

H	T	U
	6	7
+	8	4

1. Using coins   (Reminder: £1 is 100p)
Add together the one pence coins. An overview of the cluster of 7 coins at the top and 4 coins at the bottom should show you that you can make two groups of 5 (making 10) with 1 left over....... 7 + 4 = 11.

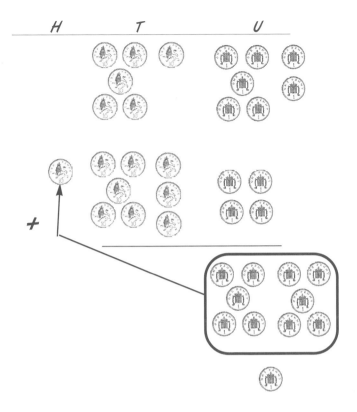

Now **TRADE** 10 one pence coins for 1 ten pence coin, leaving 1 one pence coin (units). The total for the one pence / units column is **1**. Put the traded ten pence coin in the ten pence / tens column.

Now add the ten pence coins. An overview of the cluster of 6 coins on the top line and 8 coins on the lower line shows you that you can make two groups of 5 (making 10 ten pence coins) with 5 left over (which includes the ten pence coin you just traded from the units column)............6 + 8 + 1 = 15.

The total to go in the ten pence / tens column is **5**.

TRADE the 10 ten pence coins for 1 pound (100p) coin. This **1** goes into the one pound / hundreds column.

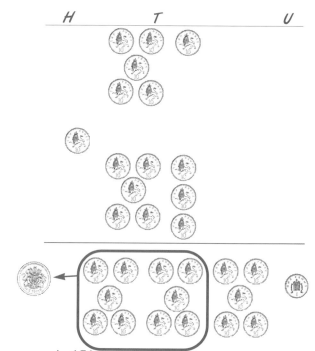

H	T	U

The answer is **151**.

2. Using place value columns

Add together the numbers in the units (U) column.
7 + 4 = 11. Eleven is 1 unit and 1 ten. Write the 1 unit
on the answer line in the units column and write 1
(actually 1 ten) at the top of the tens (T) column.

$$
\begin{array}{r}
\ \ H\ \ T\ \ U \\
6^{\,\prime}\ \ 7 \\
+\ \ 8\ \ 4 \\
\hline
1
\end{array}
$$

Answers to practise
exercise B,
questions 1 and 2
1a. 82 1b. 43
2a. 83 2b. 28
turn to page 44 for the
remaining answers

Add together the numbers in the tens (T) column.
6 + 8 + 1 = 15. Write 5 on the answer line in the
tens column.

$$
\begin{array}{r}
\ \ H\ \ T\ \ U \\
6^{\,\prime}\ \ 7 \\
+\ \ 8\ \ 4 \\
\hline
1\ \ 5\ \ 1
\end{array}
$$

Write the 1 from the 15 on the answer line in the
hundreds column.

Write the 1 from the 15 on the answer line in the
hundreds column.

```
H   T   U
    6ᐟ  7
+   8   4
1   5   1
```

The answer is **151**.

3. Using numbers on their own

Start in the units column and add together the units
numbers. 7 + 4 = 11. Write the **1** unit in the units
column on the answer line. Write 1 (actually 1 ten)
above the 6 at the top of the tens column.

```
ᐟ
67
+84
  1
```

Add the numbers in the tens column.....6 + 8 + 1 =
15. Write the **5** in the tens column on the answer line.

```
ᐟ
67
+84
 51
```

Write the **1** from the 15 on the answer line in the
hundreds column.

```
67
+87
151
```

The answer is **151**.

*Adding with trading in units / tens, tens /
hundreds and hundreds / thousands.*
  (Reminder: £1 is 100p   £10 is 1000p)

43

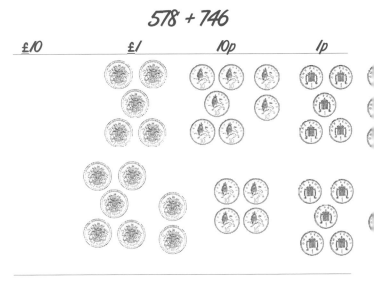

578 + 746

£10	£1	10p	1p

```
Th  H  T  U
    5  7  8          578
  +7  4  6         +746
```

1. Using coins (and £10 note)
Add together the one pence coins / units. (Look at the patterns of the 8 and 6 and see a cluster of 5 in each of these numbers. The two 5 clusters add to make 10).......
8 + 6 = 14. 14 is 4 units and 1 ten. The total in the units column is **4**.

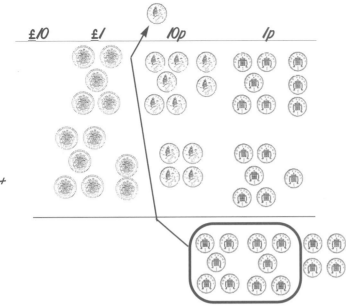

TRADE 10 one pence coins for 1 ten pence coin and put the ten pence coin in the ten pence column.
Put together the ten pence coins........7 + 4 + 1 = 12. The **2** goes as the total for the ten pence column.

TRADE the 10 ten pence coins for 1 pound (100p) coin. Put this 1 pound coin in the pounds (100) column

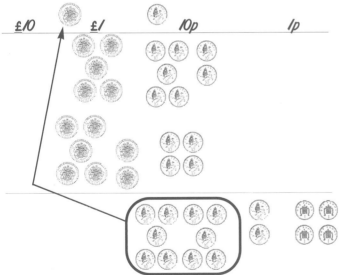

Now add together the pound coins, again looking at the pattern of 5 clusters.........
5 + 7 + 1 = 13. From these 13 coins, **3** go as the total in the one pound column and 10 coins are **TRADED** for **1** £10 note, which is placed in the £10 column.

The answer is **1324**.

2. Using place value columns

Add the two numbers in the units (U) column....
8 + 6 = 14. Fourteen is 1 ten and 4 units. Write 4 on the answer line in the units column and write 1 for the ten at the top of the tens (T) column.

```
Th  H   T   U
        5   7'  8
   +    7   4   6
                4
```

Add the numbers in the tens column.......
7 + 4 + 1 = 12.
The sum of this column is 12 tens. The 2 from the 12 is 2 tens. Write 2 on the answer line in the tens column. The 1 from the 12 is 10 tens, that is 1 hundred, so write 1 at the top of the hundreds (H) column.

```
Th  H    T   U
     5'  7'  8
  +  7   4   6
         2   4
```

Finally, add the numbers in the hundreds (H) column.......
5 + 7 + 1 = 13.
The sum of this column is 13 hundreds. The 3 from 13 is 3 hundreds, so write 3 on the answer line in the hundreds column. The 1 from the 13 is ten hundreds, that is 1 thousand, so write 1 on the answer line in the thousands (Th) column.

```
Th   H    T   U
      5'  7'  8
  +   7   4   6
  /   3   2   4
```

The answer is **1324**

3. Using numbers on their own

Start in the units column and add together the unit numbers.......8 + 6 = 14. Write the **4** units on the answer line in the units column. Write the 1 (actually a ten) from 14 above the 7 at the top of the tens column.

$$
\begin{array}{r}
5\overset{1}{7}8 \\
+746 \\
\hline
4
\end{array}
$$

Now add the numbers in the tens column (including the 1 ten carried over from adding the unit numbers)......
7 + 4 + 1 = 12. Write the **2** from the 12 on the answer line of the tens column. Write the 1 from the 12 (actually 100) above the 5 in the hundreds column.

$$
\begin{array}{r}
\overset{1}{5}\overset{1}{7}8 \\
+746 \\
\hline
24
\end{array}
$$

Now add the numbers in the hundreds column.....
5 + 7 + 1 = 13. Write the **3** from 13 on the answer line of the hundreds column and the **1** from 13 on the answer line for the thousands column.

$$
\begin{array}{r}
\overset{1}{5}\overset{1}{7}8 \\
+\ 746 \\
\hline
1324
\end{array}
$$

The answer is **1324**.

Practise exercise C

1a. 463 + 859	1b. 1322 - 859
2a. 682 + 939	2b. 1621 - 682

(Check that your answers to 1a, 1b, 2a and 2b are correct (page 49) before trying the other examples. If they are not correct, work through this section again, using coins and writing down the work).

For examples 3 to 12, look at the numbers in each question and make an estimate of the answer, as well as the "accurate" answer.

3. 777 + 444   4.   2821 - 654
5. 892 + 759   6.   6321 - 486
7. 348 + 878   8.   3427 - 1269
9. 987 + 965   10.   943 - 287
11. 1476 + 866   12.   6564 - 897
13. 1652 - 476   14.   1335 + 2898

(answers on page 51)

Adding involving a zero.

467 + 234

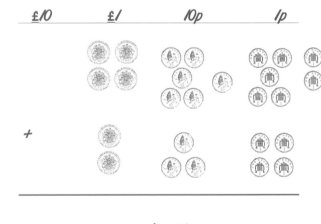

Th	H	T	U	
	4	6	7	467
+	2	3	4	+234

1. Adding with coins

Add together the one pence coins (units)......7 + 4 = 11. The total is eleven, which is 1 ten and 1 unit. **TRADE** 10 one pence coins for 1 ten pence coin. The **1** one pence coin is the answer in the units / 1p column. The 1 ten pence coin should be placed in the tens / 10p column.

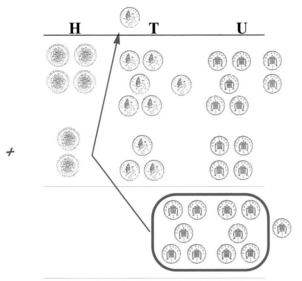

Now add together the ten pence coins, including the traded ten pence.....6 + 3 + 1 = 10. **TRADE** the 10 ten pence coins for 1 one pound coin. Put the 1 one pound coin in the £1 / hundreds column. The answer in the 10p / tens column is **0**.

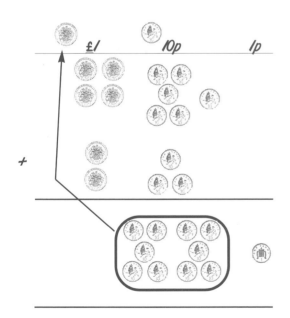

Now add the £1 coins............4 + 2 + 1 = 7. The answer in the £1 / hundreds column is **7**.

Take any three digit number, for example 461. Reverse these three digits to make a second number, 164. Subtract the smaller number from the larger number.

461
−164
297

Take the answer and reverse the three digits, 792 and add these two numbers together.

297
+792
1089

Choose some three digit numbers, try these steps and find the answers.

Answers to practise exercise C, questions 1 and 2

1a. 1322 1b. 463

2a. 1621 2b. 939

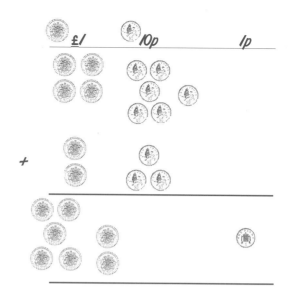

The answer is **701**.

Subtracting with a zero.

701 - 467

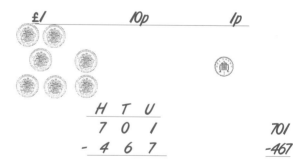

	H	T	U		
	7	0	1		701
-	4	6	7		-467

1. Subtracting with coins

This gives a clear explanation of trading (also called decomposition or renaming) when there is a zero in the top number.

Start in the units column. You have to take 7 one pence coins away from 1 one pence coin, so you have to **TRADE.** But there is a zero in the ten pence / tens column, which means that there are no ten pence coins. Trading has to move to the next place value column, the £1 column, where there are coins.

There are two trading steps:
TRADE 1 of the one pound coins for 10 ten pence coins and put them in the 10p column.

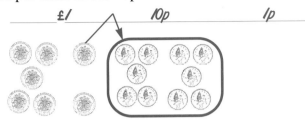

TRADE 1 of the ten pence coins for 10 one pence coins and put them in the 1p column.

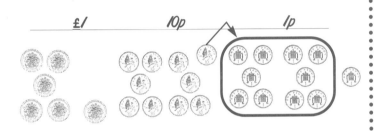

There are now 6 coins in the £1 column, 9 coins in the 10p column and 11 coins in the 1p column.

701 is now in the form

$$6 \times 100 = 600$$
$$9 \times 10 = 90$$
$$11 \times 1 = 11$$

and $600 + 90 + 11 = 701$

so the new arrangement has the same value.
You can now subtract the 467 as in previous examples and you should have 234 left.

2. Subtracting with place value columns

Start in the units (U) column. You have to subtract 7, the number in the lower line from 1, the number in the upper line. This requires that you trade to get more units in the upper line.
But there is a zero in the tens column, so there is not a ten to trade.
Move to the next place value column, the hundreds column

Answers to practise exercise C, questions 3 to 14
3. 1221 4. 2167 5. 1651
6. 5835 7. 1226 8. 2158
9. 1952 10. 656 11. 2342
12. 5667 13. 1176 14. 4233

TRADE 1 from the hundreds column to take into the tens column as 10 tens.

H	T	U
X̶6	₁0	1

TRADE 1 from the tens column to take 10 units into the units column.

H	T	U
X̶6	₁0̶9	₁1

which cleans up to be

H	T	U
6	9	₁1

The subtraction is now like the first example:
Start with the units....11 - 7 = 4. Write **4** on the answer line in the units (U) column.

The tens (T) column...9 - 6 = 3. Write **3** on the answer line in the tens (T) column.

The hundreds (H) column.....6 - 4 = 2. Write **2** on the answer line in the hundreds (H) column.

The answer is **234.**

3. Using the numbers on their own.

Start in the units column. You need to trade to be able to subtract the 7 from the 1. The tens column is zero so trading has to move to the hundreds column.

TRADE 1 from the hundreds column into 10 tens for the tens column:

X̶6 ₁0 1

This provides numbers in the tens column for the next trade.

TRADE 1 from the tens column into 10 units for the units column:

$$\cancel{7}6 \quad \cancel{7}\cancel{0}\,9 \quad 11$$

The 701 is now ready for subtraction :
Start with the units.......11 - 7 = 4. Write **4** on the answer line in the units column.

The tens......9 - 6 = 3. Write **3** on the answer line in the tens column.

The hundreds......6 - 4 = 2. Write **2** on the answer line in the units column.

$$
\begin{array}{r}
\cancel{7}6 \quad \cancel{7}\cancel{0}9 \quad 11 \\
- \quad 4 \quad\; 6 \quad\;\;\; 7 \\
\hline
2 \quad\; 3 \quad\;\;\; 4 \\
\hline
\end{array}
$$

The answer is *234*.

Practise exercise D.
1. 404 - 178   *2. 606 - 88*

(Check your answers to questions 1 and 2 now on page 54. If they are incorrect, work through this section again remembering to use the coins to help you understand each step).

3. 704 - 546   *4. 508 - 264*
5. 800 - 644   *6. 200 - 67*
7. 602 - 586   *8. 700 - 555*
9. 408 - 59   *10. 901 - 768*
                        (answers on page 55)

SUMMARY

You should now understand how to add and subtract, using trading where necessary. The same process applies to bigger numbers such as the thousands, ten thousands and all numbers.
Remember....**overview before you start**......that is, look at all the numbers in the question before you start and

1) make an estimate
2) decide if you will need to trade to get the answer.

Playing 301 in darts, Jim has to score 37 to reach zero and win. He has to end on a double (e.g. double 6, which is 12). He has three darts to throw. Work out some numbers which would take him to zero.

Don't just be 'wrong'. You can learn from your mistakes if you find out what you did and put it right.

General practise exercise E.

1. 46 + 32	2. 28 + 62
3. 87 - 54	4. 72 - 29
5. 103 - 47	6. 900 - 361
7. 483 + 159	8. 943 - 258
9. 1073 - 687	10. 4487 + 7846

(answers on page 56)

MISTAKES THAT ARE OFTEN MADE

It sometimes helps to know what might go wrong. The most common mistakes that people make when adding and subtracting are given below:

Mistakes people sometimes make when ADDING

1. Not putting the traded number into the proper place, for example;

```
  4 8 6
+2 6 7
 61413
```

an estimate would show this is impossible!

2. Not lining up place values properly, for example;

```
  2 4 8 6
+   6 4 1
  8 8 9 6
```

again an estimate would show this is impossible!

3. Making a zero mistake, for example,

```
  5 0 8
+2 6 1
  7 0 9
```

when the answer should be *769*

4. Making a basic fact mistake, for example,

$$648$$
$$+ \ 237$$
$$\overline{884}$$

when the answer should be *885*

5. Not counting in the traded ten (or hundred etc), for example,

$$764$$
$$+ \ 118$$
$$\overline{872}$$

when the answer should be *882*

Mistakes people sometimes make when SUBTRACTING

Mistakes like these can be detected if the answer is checked by adding back to see if you arrive at the original number.

1. Always taking the smaller number from the bigger number, for example,

$$563$$
$$- \ 257$$
$$\overline{314}$$

This wrong answer was obtained by taking away 3 from 7 in the units column. A ten from the 6 should have been traded to give 13 units on the top line

$$5 \quad \cancel{5}6 \quad 13$$
$$- \ 2 \quad 5 \quad 7$$
$$\overline{3 \quad 0 \quad 6}$$

and the answer should be *306*.

Some mistakes are easy to spot. Compare your answer with an estimate.

Answers to practise exercise D, questions 3 to 10

3. 158 4. 244 5. 156
6. 133 7. 16 8. 145
9. 349 10. 133

2. Taking away from zero, for example,

$$
\begin{array}{r}
708 \\
-342 \\
\hline
406
\end{array}
$$

when the answer should be *366*.

This wrong answer was obtained by taking away 4 from 0 and writing 0 as the answer. A hundred from the 7 should have been traded to give 10 tens in the tens column, as shown below;

$$
\begin{array}{r}
6\!\!\!\diagup 7 \;\; 10 \;\; 8 \\
- \; 3 \;\; 4 \;\; 2 \\
\hline
3 \;\; 6 \;\; 6
\end{array}
$$

3. Adding the two numbers instead of subtracting them. *(Especially likely in mixed addition and subtraction exercises).*

4. Basic fact mistakes, for example,

$$
\begin{array}{r}
98 \\
- 43 \\
\hline
56
\end{array}
$$

when the answer should be *55*.

Answers to practise
exercise E

1. 78 2. 90 3. 33
4. 43 5. 56 6. 539
7. 642 8. 685 9. 386
10. 12333

5. Not lining up place values properly, for example,

$$
\begin{array}{r}
956 \\
- 52 \\
\hline
436
\end{array}
$$

when the answer should be *904*.

An estimate would show this is an impossible answer

6. Forgetting part of the trading process, for example,

$$
\begin{array}{r}
4\ 3\ 1 \\
-\ 2\ 6\ 0 \\
\hline
2\ 7\ 1
\end{array}
$$

when the answer should be *171*.

This answer was obtained by forgetting to take away the 1 traded hundred from the 4 hundred in the top number. The correct procedure is;

$$
\begin{array}{r}
3\!\!\!/\!4\ \ /3\ \ 1 \\
-\ \ \ 2\ \ \ 6\ \ 0 \\
\hline
1\ \ \ 7\ \ 1
\end{array}
$$

SUMMARY SO FAR:

You have looked at;

Place value
For example in **2583**, **2** is 2 thousands, **5** is 5 hundreds, **8** is 8 tens and **3** is 3 units

and in **3852**, **3** is 3 thousands, **8** is 8 hundreds, **5** is 5 tens and **2** is 2 units
The value a digit has depends on its place in the whole number....place value.

Trading

This relates to place value and is used in addition and subtraction sums.

For example, trading takes 1 hundred and trades it for 10 tens, or 1 ten and trades it for 10 units or, in reverse, trading takes 10 tens and trades them for 1 hundred, or 10 units and trades them for 1 ten.

Basic facts

These are all the addition and subtraction facts for the numbers 0 to 10. They are all inter-related and one fact can be used to work out another. This helps memorising the facts and also shows how numbers can be used efficiently (and easily). Also remember to look for numbers within numbers (e.g. 7 is 5 + 2).

Written methods for addition and subtraction

The methods are the same, but reversed and can involve trading. You do need to understand place value to be good at these sums.

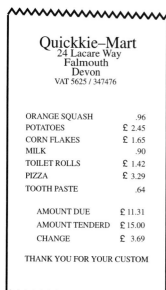

Quickkie–Mart
24 Lacare Way
Falmouth
Devon
VAT 5625 / 347476

ORANGE SQUASH	.96
POTATOES	£ 2.45
CORN FLAKES	£ 1.65
MILK	.90
TOILET ROLLS	£ 1.42
PIZZA	£ 3.29
TOOTH PASTE	.64
AMOUNT DUE	£ 11.31
AMOUNT TENDERD	£ 15.00
CHANGE	£ 3.69

THANK YOU FOR YOUR CUSTOM

ADDING UP COLUMNS OF NUMBERS

Adding up a lot of numbers, like a shopping bill, a restaurant bill or accounts can be made easier by using either of the two methods described below. You will have to try them to find which is the better one for you.

Method 1. " Tens tallies."

Work through this example. Copy the numbers onto paper and follow each step.

The principle is to use a tally for each time you reach 10, counting on in units only.

```
  4 6
  5 5
  2 3
+ 9 8
───────
```

Start at the top in the units column and add down.
6 + 5 = 11
Eleven is 1 ten and 1 unit, so put a tally through the 5 to represent the 10.

```
  4 6
  5 5
  2 3
+ 9 8
───────
```

Now carry on down the units column, starting with the
1 unit from the eleven.
1 + 3 = 4
4 + 4 = 12

```
  4 6
  5 5
  2 3
+ 9 8
───────
      2
```

Twelve is 1 ten and 2 units so put a tally mark through the 8 to represent this 10. Write **2** on the answer line in the units column.

There are two 'ten tallies' in the units column to transfer to the tens column. Write 2 at the top of the tens column.

```
  2
  4 6
  5 5
  2 3
+ 9 8
───────
      2
```

Now add down the tens column.
2 + 4 = 6
6 + 5 = 11. Use a tally to mark the 10 from this eleven.

```
  2
  4 6
  5 5
  2 3
+ 9 8
───────
  2 2
```

Carry on adding down the tens column, using the 1 unit from the eleven.
1 + 2 = 3
3 + 9 = 12. Use a tally to mark the 10 from this 12. Write 2 from the 12 on the answer line in the tens column

Count the tallies in the tens column. There are 2. This 2 is actually 2 hundreds (200). Write 2 on the answer line in the hundreds column.

```
    2
  4 6
  5 5
  2 3
+ 9 8
2 2 2
```

The answer is *222.*

Work through the next two examples.

```
    3
  8 7
  7 6
  6 9
+ 8 8
3 2 0
```

```
    3
  5 6
  3 2
  8 7
  6 7
  9 1
  2 5
+ 4 8
4 0 6
```

Checking by estimating

Look at the 7 numbers in the last example. Of these 7 two digit numbers, 3 were significantly above 50, 1 was close to 50 and 2 were below 50.

For two digit numbers, that is from 10 to 99, 50 is an easy number to use as an approximate average value. (In this particular example the average could be a little more than 50).

As a rough check on the answer:

There are 7 two digit numbers with an average of about 50.
The total must be approximately 7 x 50 = 350.

Since we overviewed the numbers and gauged the average to be a little more than 50, the answer might be more than 350.

Remember to estimate first when trying this practise example.

38
41
83
76
48   *Estimate:* There are 10
27   two digit numbers, fairly
52   evenly distributed around 50
85
17
+ 42   Estimate at 10 x 50 = *500.*

Working accurately with tallies:

4
38
41
83
76
48
27
52
85
17
42
509

Method 2. 'Taking out tens.'

For this method you need to know the number bonds for 10 (4 + 6, etc). These need to be extended to combinations of three numbers (which add to make 10), for example, 5 + 4 + 1 and preferably some of the three number combinations which add to make 20, such as: 8 + 7 + 5 and 8 + 8 + 4.

Number bonds for 10

0+10
1+9
2+8
3+7
4+6
5+5
6+4
7+3
8+2
9+1
10+0

The idea is to scan down a column of digits and take out the pairs / combinations which make 10 and tally each 10 taken out.

For example:

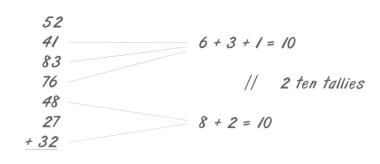

```
    52
    41 ——————————————— 6 + 3 + 1 = 10
    83
    76                    //   2 ten tallies
    48
    27 ——————————————— 8 + 2 = 10
  + 32
  _____
```

The two numbers left from the units column are 2 and 7 and 2 + 7 = 9. Write **9** on the answer line in the units column and write **2** (tens) at the top of the tens column. Now look at the tens column:

```
                              2
                             52
   8 + 2  =  10              41
                             83
   4 + 4 + 2 = 10           76
                             48
   7 + 3 = 10               27
                           + 32
/// 3 hundred tallies          9
```

There are 3 tens tallies and a digit 5 remains. Write this **5** on the answer line in the tens column and write **3** for the three tallies on the answer line in the hundreds column.

```
        52
        41
        83
        76
        48
        27
      + 32
      _____
      359
```

The answer is *359*.

Check against the estimate of 7 two digit numbers...
7 x 50 = 350.

Now look at a second example, the units column first:

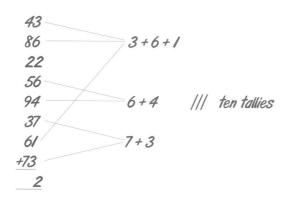

```
43
86          3 + 6 + 1
22
56
94          6 + 4      ///  ten tallies
37
61          7 + 3
+73
 2
```

Now look at the tens column:

```
                              3
                             43
    8 + 2 = 10 ───────────── 86
                             22
                           ─ 56
9 + 6 + 5 = 20 ───────────── 94
                             37
    7 + 3 = 10 ───────────── 61
                           + 73

//// four hundred           472
      tallies
```

There were 4 'ten tallies' in the tens column and 3 + 4 = 7 left. Write **7** on the answer line in the tens column and **4** on the answer line in the hundreds column.

Check against an **estimate**. There are eight numbers with 4 significantly above 50 so 50 x 8 = **400** will be a **low estimate**.

Practise exercise, F
Choose the method you prefer and practise. If you are
not sure which method you prefer, you might like to try
both methods to see which is easier for you.

1.		2.	
	42		89
	61		15
	88		75
	37		23
	94		61
	23		23
	+75		+24

*Check your answers to questions 1 and 2 (page 65). If
you are correct carry on to the remaining questions. If
you have made a mistake, check your working and/or
work through the explanations again.*

3.		4.	
	71		45
	69		56
	22		87
	44		50
	14		68
	+72		+25

5.		6.	
	32		19
	90		88
	62		72
	55		54
	68		47
	25		21
	+81		+36

7.		8.	
	16		67
	33		23
	92		49
	24		82
	27		84
	42		66
	+35		+49

9.	97	10.	55
	18		73
	61		69
	28		81
	46		28
	39		15
	21		21
	34		56
	89		32
	+ 25		+ 88

(answers on page 67)

Make up some more examples for yourself. Try asking someone to give you some two digit numbers or take all the pence values of a supermarket bill (you will get a lot of 9s) and add them up or break up telephone numbers into two digits, or use playing cards (page 18).

MENTAL ARITHMETIC.....WORKING 'IN YOUR HEAD'

Doing sums in your head, mental arithmetic, requires several skills which often make written methods second best. Not least of these skills is memory, especially short term memory.

Consequently the methods described below are adaptations to make mental work easier. Because the procedures are different, you will need to practise and persevere, but learning these new strategies will further help your understanding of numbers and arithmetic.

1. ADDING 9's

One of the best things about 9 is that it is 1 less than 10 and 10 is an easy number to add.

This strategy uses two easy steps instead of one hard step.

It is also an estimate followed by an adjustment of the estimate.

Answers to column addition, practise exercise, F questions 1 and 2

1. 420 2. 310

$$9 = 10-1$$

$$99 = 100-1$$

To add 9:
1. Add 10
2. Subtract 1.
(because adding 9 gives a smaller answer than adding 10)

For example;
76 + 9   is done in two steps

1. 76 + 10 = 86
2. 86 - 1 = 85

for   64 + 9

1. 64 + 10 = 74
2. 74 - 1 = 73

To add 99:
1. Add 100
2. Subtract 1

For example;
874 + 99 is done in two steps

1. 874 + 100 = 974
2. 974 - 1 = 973

and 697 + 99
1. 697 + 100 = 797
2. 797 - 1 = 796

To add 95:
1. Add 100
2. Subtract 5

For example;
578 + 95 is done in two steps

1. 578 + 100 = 678
2. 678 - 5 = 673

and 1866 + 95

1. 1866 + 100 = 1966
2. 1966 - 5 = 1961

To add 998:
1. Add 1000
2. Subtract 2

For example;
6579 + 998 is done in two steps

1. 6579 + 1000 = 7579
2. 7579 - 2 = 7577

and 1297 + 998

1. 1297 + 1000 = 2297
2. 2297 - 2 = 2295

This procedure can be adapted to many numbers near to 10, 100, 1000 and so on.

It can also be used with money, especially those prices which are so popular in shops such as £9-99, £19-99 and so on.

For example;
add together the following prices

£4-99	this is £5 less 1p
£9-99	this is £10 less 1p
£3-99	this is £4 less 1p
£5-99	this is £6 less 1p

Answers to column addition, practise exercise, F questions 3 to 10

3. 292 4. 331 5. 413
6. 337 7. 269 8. 420
9. 458 10. 518

Step 1. Add the (rounded up) pounds

£5 + £10 + £4 + £6 = £25

Step 2. Subtract the 4 x 1p (= 4p)

£25 minus 4p = *£24-96*

Books used to be priced as £5-95, £6-95, £14-95 and so on. The same strategy can be used for 95p prices, for example;

add together the following prices

£4-95	which is £5 less 5p
£5-95	which is £6 less 5p
£3-95	which is £4 less 5p
£9-95	which is £10 less 5p
£4-95	which is £5 less 5p

Step 1. Add the (rounded up) pounds

£5 + £6 + £4 + £10 + £5 = £30

Step 2. Subtract 5 x 5p (= 25p) from £30

£30 minus 25p = *£29-75.*

Practise exercise, G

Add together the prices.

1. £9-99 + £10-99 + £8-99 + £4-99 + £9-99
2. £4-99 + £4-99 + £4-99

Check the answers to these two questions (on page 70) before trying the rest. If you have made a mistake, check through your working and if you are still unsure read through the method again, trying out the examples with money.

3. £4·95 + £4·95 + £9·95 + £9·95
4. £19·95 + £14·95 + £24·95 + £29·95 + £9·95 + £4·95
5. £99·95 + £49·95
6. £1·99 + 99p + £2·99 + £1·99 + £4·99

(answers on page 71)

Subtracting 9's

The same idea is used, that is two easy steps instead of one hard step. The first easy step is subtracting 10 and the second easy step is adding 1.

Since 10 is bigger than 9, when you subtract 10 you get a smaller answer. The readjustment is made by **adding** back 1.

Try this with some coins, for example, start with 57p set up as four 10p coins (40p) and seventeen 1p coins (17p).

Procedure 1

Take away nine 1p coins to give an answer of *48*

Procedure 2

Step 1. Take away one 10p coin

This leaves 47p

Step 2. Add one 1p coin

giving an answer of *48.*

Try this with some other examples, using coins AND numbers each time.

To subtract 9

Step 1. Subtract 10
Step 2. Add 1

For example 57 - 9

Step 1.   57 - 10 = 47
Step 2.   47 + 1 = **48**

To subtract 90

Step 1.   Subtract 100
Step 2.   Add 10

Work this through with £1 and 10p coins. The process uses the fact £1 - 10p = 90p.

Example 1; 684 - 90

Step 1. 684 - 100 = 584
Step 2. 584 + 10 = *594*

Example 2; 5879 - 90

Step 1. 5879 - 100 = 5779
Step 2. 5779 + 10 = *5789*

Compare the two steps used to ADD 9 to the two steps used to SUBTRACT 9

Answers to practise exercise G, 'Add together the prices' questions 1 and 2

1. £44.95 2. £14.97

To subtract 95

Step 1.   Subtract 100
Step 2.   Add 5

For example: 673 - 95
Step 1.   673 - 100 = 573
Step 2.   573 + 5 = *578*

To subtract 990

Step 1. Subtract 1000
Step 2. Add 10

For example: 7864 - 990

Step 1.   7864 - 1000 = 6864
Step 2.   6864 + 10 = *6874*

To subtract 8

Step 1.   Subtract 10
Step 2.   Add 2

For example:

Step 1.   64 - 8 = 54
Step 2.   54 + 2 = 56

This procedure can be adapted to many numbers near to 10, 100, 1000 etc.

Answers to practise exercise, G
'Add together the prices'
questions 3 to 6
   3. £29.80 4. £104.70
   5. £149.90 6. £12.95

71

2. GENERAL ADDITION

The demands on memory of mental arithmetic can sometimes be reduced by using methods which offer more support. For example, one of the ways people use to help remember something is to repeat it (sometimes out loud) several times.

We read numbers from left to right. For example, 645 is said as 'six hundred and forty five'. However, in written arithmetic we add from right to left (units, tens, hundreds, etc).

In mental addition if you add from left to right, you start with what is effectively an estimate and repeat the early numbers as you work through the example, thus supporting short term memory.

Always overview the question before you start. Look at the values of the numbers, form a very broad estimate, see if there is any trading.

Adding with no trading:

Example: *134 + 632*

Hundreds. Start with the hundreds....add 1 hundred to 6 hundred... 1 + 6 = 7......

so we have seven hundred and.......

Tens. Add the tens....3 tens add 3 tens.... 3 + 3 = 6......so we have seven hundred and sixty.......

Units. Add the units...4 + 2 = 6....so the answer is seven hundred and sixty six

134 + 632 = 766.

As we worked through this problem, we repeated seven hundred three times and seven hundred and sixty twice. We also constructed the answer **in the same order** as its final form (with right to left addition, the digits are constructed in reverse).

Adding with trading:

Example: **462 + 379**

Hundreds. Start with the hundreds and add....4 + 3 = 7...the answer so far is **seven hundred.**

Tens. Add the tens digits..... 6 + 7 = 13 tens

13 tens are 130 which is 1 hundred and 30, so the 1 hundred should be added to

the existing 7 hundred....7 + 1 = 8 hundred

The answer so far is **eight hundred and thirty**......

Units. Add the units digits....... 2 + 9 = 11 units

11 units are 1 ten and 1 unit, so the 1 ten should be added to the existing thirty to make forty.

The final answer is *841.*

Practise exercise H.

Try adding these examples in your head.

1.	*45 + 43*	*2.*	*67 + 32*
3.	*36 + 47*	*4.*	*78 + 15*
5.	*453 + 346*	*6.*	*134 + 762*
7.	*673 + 264*	*8.*	*332 + 291*
9.	*775 + 366*	*10.*	*609 + 494*

GENERAL SUBTRACTION

The written method we used for subtraction is quite demanding as a mental arithmetic method. It requires an ability to visualise and hold that image in memory compounded by the several steps involved in the method.

There are some 'special cases', but first, as with addition, look at a method which works (or subtracts) from left to right.

1. Subtracting from left to right.

Overview to see if this is an example which would require trading.

Example 1:   *487 - 163*

Hundreds. Subtract the hundreds.....4 - 1 = 3 hundreds. The answer so far is three hundred and.....

Tens. Subtract the tens.....8 - 6 = 2 tens. The answer so far is three hundred and twenty.......

Units. Subtract the units.....7 - 3 = 4 units. The final answer is three hundred and twenty four......*324.*

Example 2:   *632 - 186*

Hundreds. Subtract the hundreds.....6 - 1 = five hundreds. The answer so far is five hundred and......

Tens. Subtract the tens....3 - 8...this requires trading. Reduce the hundreds to four hundred and move the hundred (= 10 tens) to the tens column...13 - 8 = 5. The answer so far is four hundred and fifty......

Units. Subtract the units....2 - 6...this requires trading. Reduce the tens to forty and move the ten (=10 units) to the units column.......12 - 6 = 6. The final answer is four hundred and forty six......*446.*

Any new skill requires practise. Arithmetic skills are no exception. These new procedures may feel strange at first. Do try to persevere and give them time to work.

2. Counting on

This strategy works particularly well with subtractions from 100s, 1000s, 10 000s, etc. Number bonds for 10 are especially useful in these cases.

Start with the units digit from the subtracting number. When you first work through these examples, use coins (and trading) to show the procedure.

Example 1:   6000 - 2349

Units. Start with the 9 (from 2349)

           Add *1* to 9 to make 10   2349 becomes 2350

Tens.   Add *5* to 5 (from 2350) to make 10

                           2350 becomes 2400

Hundreds.   Add *6* to 4 (from 2400) to make 10

                           2400 becomes 3000

Thousands. Add *3* to 3 (from 3000) to make 6

                           3000 becomes 6000

You have counted on *3* thousands, *6* hundreds, *5* tens and *1* unit

The answer is *3651*.

6000 - 2349 = 3651

Check... 2349
+ 3651
6000

Example 2:   800 - 312

Units.   312 +   *8* = 320

Tens.   320 + *80* = 400

Hundreds.   400 + *400* = 800

The answer is *488*.

Check.   312
+488
800

Answers to practise exercise H.
1. 88 2. 99 3. 83
4. 93 5. 799 6. 896
7. 937 8. 623
9. 1141 10. 1103

Now try an example with money:

£20 - £13.26

One pence.   £13.26 + *4p* = £13.30

Ten pence.   £13.30 + *70p* = £14.00

One pound.   £14.00 + *£6* = £20.00

The answer is *£6.74*   Check   £13.26
                                     + £ 6.74
                                       £20.00

Practise exercise 1.

1.   500 - 327   *2.   700 - 482*

Check your answers to these two questions on page 79.
If they are correct carry on with questions 3 to 12. If
they are not correct, work through the examples again,
remembering to use the coins first run through.

3.   1000 - 609   *4.   800 - 333*

5.   £10.00 - £3.95   *6.   £20.00 - £16.45*

7.   £100.00 - £67.36 *8.   2000 - 1812*

9.   300 - 87   *10.   £5.00 - £2.12*

11. £5000 - £1756.50   *12.   4000 - 2614*

(answers on page 80)

3. Equal additions with tens

This is also a written method. It is easy to explain if you use algebra, but not as easy to explain with coins. It is an alternative to trading.

The basic idea is to add ten to the units column of the top number and balance this by adding ten to the tens column of the bottom number.

For example, *86 - 38*

Step 1.   Add a ten units to the top number

$$
\begin{array}{cc}
8 & 16 \\
-3 & 8 \\
\hline
\end{array}
$$

Step 2.   Add ten to the bottom number in the tens column.

$$
\begin{array}{cc}
8 & 16 \\
-34 & 8 \\
\hline
\end{array}
$$

Step 3.   Subtract

$$
\begin{array}{cc}
8 & 16 \\
-34 & 8 \\
\hline
4 & 8 \\
\hline
\end{array}
$$

Check

$$
\begin{array}{r}
48 \\
+38 \\
\hline
86 \\
\hline
\end{array}
$$

Equal additions can be shown not to change the answer by using algebra. If the numbers being subtracted are a - b. Equal addition of 10 makes this

(a + 10) - (b + 10)

This becomes

a + 10 - b - 10

which is a - b.

The method works for all place values, for example

438 - 173

Step 1. Subtract in the units column 8 - 3 = **5**

$$
\begin{array}{r}
438 \\
- 173 \\
\hline
5 \\
\hline
\end{array}
$$

Step 2. Add ten tens (100) to the top digit in the tens column, making 3 tens into 13 tens.

Subtract....13 - 7 = **6**

$$\begin{array}{ccc} 4 & 13 & 8 \\ -1 & 7 & 3 \\ \hline & 6 & 5 \end{array}$$

Step 3. Add the (equal) one hundred to the 1 (hundred) on the bottom line to make 2 hundred. Subtract in the hundreds column.....4 - 2 = **2**

$$\begin{array}{ccc} 4 & 13 & 8 \\ -2\!\!\!/1 & 7 & 3 \\ \hline 2 & 6 & 5 \end{array}$$

The answer is **265.**

Check

$$\begin{array}{r} 265 \\ +173 \\ \hline 438 \end{array}$$

Equal additions can be used in more than one column.

For example,   *614 - 378*

Step 1.

$$\begin{array}{ccc} 6 & 1 & 14 \\ -3 & 2\!\!\!/1 & 8 \\ \hline & & 6 \end{array}$$

equal additions for the units

Step 2.

$$\begin{array}{ccc} 6 & 11 & 14 \\ -4\!\!\!/3 & 2\!\!\!/1 & 8 \\ \hline 2 & 9 & 6 \end{array}$$

equal additions for the tens

Answers to examples 1 and 2 from Practise Exercise 1
1. 173 2. 218

Check

$$\begin{array}{r} 296 \\ +318 \\ \hline 614 \end{array}$$

4. Balance and adjust

This is a similar strategy to rounding up 9 to 10. The idea is to make the subtraction easier and then adjust back. You make it two easy steps by changing the sum.

Example, *86 - 38*

Step 1.

$$\begin{array}{r} 86 \\ -38 \\ \hline \end{array}$$

Make the units column subtraction easier by 'balancing'. The adjustment should make the answer in the units column 0. So here you add 2 to the top number.

$$\begin{array}{r} 88 \\ -38 \\ \hline \end{array}$$

Step 2. Subtract

$$\begin{array}{r} 88 \\ -38 \\ \hline 50 \end{array}$$

Step 3. This intermediate answer (an estimate) is too big since the top number was made bigger. To adjust back to a precise answer, subtract the 2 you added in Step 1.

$$50 - 2 = 48$$

The answer is *48*.

Answers to questions 3–12, practise exercise 1
3. *391* 4. *467*
5. *£6.05* 6. *£3.55*
7. *£32.64* 8. *188*
9. *213* 10. *£2.88*
11. *£3243.50*
12. *1386*

Practise examples J.
1. *73 - 27*   2. *94 - 68*   3. *51 - 36*
4. *67 - 38*   5. *81 - 34*   6. *42 - 17*

-	0	1	2	3	4	5	6	7	8	9	10
0	0	1	2	3	4	5	6	7	8	9	10
1	1	2	3	4	5	6	7	8	9	10	11
2	2	3	4	5	6	7	8	9	10	11	12
3	3	4	5	6	7	8	9	10	11	12	13
4	4	5	6	7	8	9	10	11	12	13	14
5	5	6	7	8	9	10	11	12	13	14	15
6	6	7	8	9	10	11	12	13	14	15	16
7	7	8	9	10	11	12	13	14	15	16	17
8	8	9	10	11	12	13	14	15	16	17	18
9	9	10	11	12	13	14	15	16	17	18	19
0	10	11	12	13	14	15	16	17	18	19	20

The square of facts

Table Square
please cut out or
photocopy this
page and use it to
test yourself

	0	1	2	3	4	5	6	7	8	9	10
0											
1											
2											
3											
4											
5											
6											
7											
8											
9											
10											

	0	1	2	3	4	5	6	7	8	9	10
0											
1											
2											
3											
4											
5											
6											
7											
8											
9											
10											